Hello Kitty®
Glitter Clay
Activity Book

by Deborah Schecter

Scholastic Inc.

New York Toronto London Auckland Sydney
Mexico City New Delhi Hong Kong Buenos Aires

Design by Lee Kaplan
Illustrations by Yancey C. Labat
Photography by Rocco Melillo

ISBN 0-439-32836-5

12 11 10 9 8 7 6 5 4 3 2 1   1 2 3 4 5 6/0

Printed in the U.S.A.
First Scholastic printing, October 2001

Table of Contents

Dear **Hello Kitty** Club Member,

Welcome to a fun-filled book of clay-modeling projects, starring your friend Hello Kitty and her pal Kathy! With your special shaped cutters and colorful, sparkly glitter clay, you'll join these two best friends as they share all kinds of fun times together. From baking yummy cookies to getting ready for a super-fun sleepover, there's so much to make and do!

You'll also celebrate special times with Hello Kitty all year long—plan a surprise party for her birthday, dress her up for New Year's Eve, go on a shopping spree, have fun at the beach, and lots, lots more.

The projects in this book are sure to spark other ideas, too. Ready to get started? Turn the page and get going!

Get Ready for

Hello Kitty Glitter Clay Fun

This book has lots of fun ideas for easy clay projects that you can do.

Helpful Hints

- Spread wax paper over the area where you're going to work. Or you can use newspaper. Just be careful not to press the clay too hard into the newspaper because it might pick up the print.

- Wear an old shirt or smock to protect your clothes.

- Keep a cup of water nearby. Wet the tips of your fingers to help pieces of clay stick together and to smooth cracks.

- Be careful while you're working with the glitter clay, or else the glitter will get all over you. Also, wash your hands when you're finished with a project.

- When you're working on a project, keep the clay you're not using in a plastic bag or plastic wrap to keep it from drying out. Do the same for leftover clay and unfinished projects.

- When you're finished with a project, let it dry overnight. Thicker pieces may take longer to dry.

These tools will come in handy when you work with glitter clay:

Plastic knife

Colored toothpicks

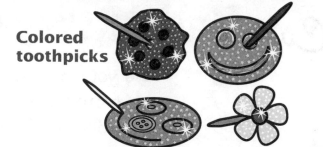

Use buttons, **fat crayons**, **pencils**, and **empty spools of thread** to make imprints.

Wrap clay around **twist ties** or **toothpicks** to give an object support or to help it stand up.

To help two thick pieces hold together, connect them with a piece of **toothpick**.

- Use craft glue to attach bits of yarn, sequins, paper, tiny buttons, and other decorations to projects. Glue can also be used to mend cracks and clay pieces if they break off.

- When you need more clay, you can mix up your own! Look on page 43 for an easy recipe!

Cute Hello Kitty Cutouts

Use your cutters to create cute cutouts of Hello Kitty and Kathy!

What You Do:

1. Spread newspaper where you're going to work.

 **2.** Roll a piece of clay into a ball. Then flatten it with your hand to make a round shape.

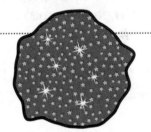

3. Press one of your cutters into the clay.

4. Gently lift the clay-filled cutter out of the excess clay.

5. Gently lift the clay shape out of the cutter, using a toothpick if necessary.

6. Flip the cutter over and press the other side of the cutter into your shape to imprint the design into the clay.

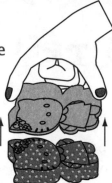

What You Need

- **Newspaper**
- **Glitter clay**
- **Assorted Hello Kitty cutters**
- **Toothpicks**

You can make lots of Hello Kitty projects with your Hello Kitty cutters and glitter clay.

Design pretty outfits for Hello Kitty to wear.

Turn the page to find out how.

Dress Up Hello Kitty!

Hello Kitty is a fashion princess. You can dress her up in colorful outfits made of clay!

What You Do:

1. Make a clay cutout of Hello Kitty using your full body cutter. Let the clay dry.

2. Pick an outfit for Hello Kitty to wear. Place a piece of lightweight paper over one of the patterns below. Trace it and then cut it out.

3. Flatten a piece of clay. Place the pattern on the clay. Use a plastic knife to cut around the pattern into the clay. Then lift off the pattern.

4. Use bits of different-colored clay to decorate Hello Kitty's outfit. Add a cute collar, pretty pockets, fancy flowers, and other decorations. Use a toothpick to make designs, too.

5. Don't forget a bow! Make different-colored bows for Hello Kitty using the pattern on the left.

6. Let the outfits dry. Then dress up your Hello Kitty cutout!

What You Need
- **Hello Kitty full body cutter**
- **Clay**
- **Lightweight paper and pencil**
- **Scissors**
- **Plastic knife**
- **Toothpicks**

How does Hello Kitty wake up and start her day?

Turn the page to find out!

Wake Up, Hello Kitty!

Hello Kitty wakes up to the *brrring* of her alarm clock. You can make Hello Kitty's alarm clock to help her start her day.

What You Do:

1. To make the clock face, pick a color of clay, roll a little ball of it, and then flatten it a little bit.

2. Roll a thin string of another color of clay. Press it around the clock face.

3. Use black and red clay to make itty-bitty clock hands. Press them onto the clock face.

4. Add three legs to make the clock stand up. You can connect the legs to the clock with pieces of toothpicks if you need to.

5. You can even put a bell on top of the clock, if you like.

What You Need

- Clay
- Toothpicks

Brrring-brrring! **It's time to get up, Hello Kitty! Breakfast is almost ready.**

Hello Kitty's Breakfast

Help Hello Kitty's mama make a yummy breakfast for Hello Kitty.

What You Do:

1. First make a frying pan. Flatten a little ball of black clay.

Use your fingers to pinch up the sides. Then shape a handle.

2. Fry up some eggs. Flatten two little circles of white clay.

Press a tiny yellow ball of clay in the center of each.

3. Toast the bread. Make little rectangles of brown clay.

Use yellow or red clay to spread "butter" or "jam" on top.

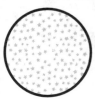

4. Now help to set the table. Flatten balls of clay to make plates.

Shape pieces of clay into forks, spoons, and knives.

What else might Hello Kitty have for breakfast? O.J.? Cereal? Use your imagination to make other things.

What You Need

- Clay

Hello Kitty's best friend, Kathy, is coming over to bake cookies!

Turn the page to help them!

Hello Kitty Bakes

Hello Kitty's best friend, Kathy, is coming over! Hello Kitty will make some yummy snacks!

What You Do:

1. Make a clay cutout and imprint of Hello Kitty.

2. Make a mixing bowl: Roll a ball of clay. Use your thumb to press a hole in the middle of the ball. Then pinch around the sides with your fingers to make a bowl shape.

3. Mix up the cookie dough. What kind do you want to make? (Hello Kitty loves chocolate chip cookies!) Mix some brown and white clay together until they are blended. Pat the clay into the mixing bowl. Add itty-bitty chocolate chips using dark brown clay.

4. Hello Kitty needs a cookie sheet. Fold a piece of aluminum foil into a rectangle. Turn up one edge, as shown.

5. Roll little balls of clay cookie dough and put them on the cookie sheet.

6. While the cookies are baking, make a pretty platter to put them on. Flatten a ball of clay. Then press your flower cutter into the clay. Use a toothpick to lift out the shape.

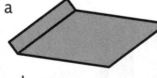

7. Mmmm! Something smells good! The cookies must be done. Flatten little balls of light brown clay and dot them with dark brown clay chocolate chips. Then put the cookies on your platter.

What You Need

- **Hello Kitty full body cutter**
- **Flower cutter**
- **Clay**
- **Aluminum foil**
- **Toothpick**

Here's More: You can make an oven for Hello Kitty to bake her cookies in!

1. Cut off the side flaps from a small, empty teabag box.

CUT   CUT

2. Cut a piece of construction paper to fit around the box. Cut a piece of paper to cover the outside of the top flap, too. Then glue the paper to the box.

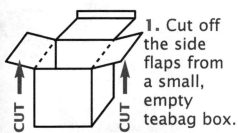

3. Use a marker to draw burners on the stovetop and a handle on the oven door. Now it's time to put the cookies in!

Hello Kitty and Kathy still have a lot to do! They are planning a tea party.

11

Hello Kitty *and* Kathy's Tea Party

Tea parties are so much fun!

What You Do:

 1. Start with the teapot and cups. To make the teapot, first roll a ball of clay.

 Shape a spout and a handle. Use a toothpick to gently poke a hole in the handle. Then make a top for the teapot.

2. Teacups come next! Use your finger to make a hole in the middle of a little ball of clay.

Then press around the sides to make a cup shape. around the sides to make a cup shape. Pinch the clay on one side of the cup to make a handle.

3. Use your flower cutter to make flower-shaped saucers! To make a place for the

 cup to sit, gently press the end of a fat crayon into each saucer.

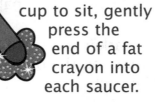 (Make extra daisy-shaped plates for the cookies!)

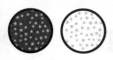

4. Mama has made a surprise. She has baked cupcakes for Hello Kitty and Kathy's tea party! Roll little balls of brown and white clay. Shape them like cupcakes.

5. For frosting, flatten little balls of brown, pink, or white clay. Press these on top of the cupcakes. To add a squiggle of frosting, roll a long string piece of clay. Zigzag it on top of the cupcakes!

What You Need

- Clay
- Toothpick
- Flower cutter
- Fat crayon (optional)

13

Where should Hello Kitty and Kathy hold their tea party?

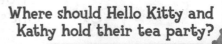
How about the garden?

Hello Kitty's Garden

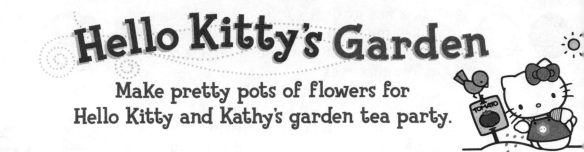

Make pretty pots of flowers for
Hello Kitty and Kathy's garden tea party.

To Make a Pretty Flowerpot:

 Roll a ball of clay.

Use your thumb to make a hole in the middle of the clay ball. Pinch around the sides to make a flowerpot shape.

Then make a frilly border with your fingertips.

To Make a Swirly Flowerpot:

Mix together pieces of two different colors of clay. Stop mixing them when the colors are partly blended.

To Make a Rainbow Flowerpot:

Use several colors of clay to make long strings. Press them together to form a rectangle.

Bring together the two ends of the clay rectangle and press them together. Flatten a ball of clay for the bottom of the flowerpot. Press it into place.

Decorate your flowerpots with polka dots, stripes, or other designs. You can come up with your own kinds of flowerpots, too!

To Make Flowers:

1. Use your flower cutter to make flowers. Try making the petals one color and the centers another color.

2. Break a green toothpick in half. Press your flower onto the end of a toothpick half. Let it dry flat.

3. Now try designing your own kinds of flowers. Press each one onto a toothpick half and let it dry flat.

4. "Plant" your flowers. Press a ball of brown clay "soil" into each flowerpot. Stick your flowers into the soil.

5. Put out the teapot, cups and saucers, and plates, too. (See page 12.) Don't forget the cookies and cupcakes (pages 10–11.)

Ding, dong! **There's the doorbell. The guests for Hello Kitty's tea party are here!**

What You Need

- ● **Clay**
- ● **Flower cutter**
- ● **Green toothpicks**
  (or if you only have plain toothpicks, you can paint them green and wait for them to dry)

Hello Kitty's Sleepover

Hello Kitty is so excited. Kathy is sleeping over!

What You Do:

1. Make a clay cutout of Hello Kitty. Then make a nightgown for her to wear. Trace and cut out the pattern here.

2. Flatten some clay. Place the pattern on the clay and use a plastic knife to cut it out.

3. Help Hello Kitty get ready for bed. Put on her nightgown. Don't forget her slippers! Trace and cut out the pattern here.

4. Hello Kitty and Kathy are ready for a late-night snack of pizza and popcorn at their sleepover.

Make a Pizza!

 Flatten a ball of white clay.

 Dab on red clay for tomato sauce.

 Add bits of white clay for cheese.

Pop Some Corn!

First, make a bowl. Use your thumb to make an indent in the middle of a ball of clay.

 Then pinch around the sides to make a bowl shape.

For popcorn, fill the bowl with itty-bitty balls of yellow and white clay that you have stuck together.

What You Need

- **Hello Kitty full–body cutter**
- **Clay**
- **Paper and pencil**
- **Scissors**
- **Plastic knife**

It's been a full day. Now it's time to turn out the lights and go to bed.

Hey, who's that giggling in the dark?

Good Night, Hello Kitty!

Make a cozy bed for Hello Kitty to sleep in and a dresser for her clothes.

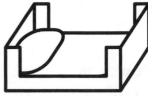

Bed

Cut the sides of a large, empty matchbox as you see here. For a soft mattress, line the box with facial tissues. Fold up a tissue to make a fluffy pillow. Add a blanket made from a colored napkin or scrap of fabric.

Dresser

1. Stack three small, empty matchboxes. Make sure the compartments inside all face the same way. (To check, push each box open.) Then glue the boxes together.

2. Cut a piece of construction paper to fit around the boxes. Then wrap it around the boxes and glue it in place.

3. Use a marker to draw a knob on each drawer. Now Hello Kitty has a dresser with drawers that open and close!

A Cuddly Friend

Hello Kitty can't go to bed without her favorite teddy bear!

 1. Roll one medium brown ball for the head.

 2. Use your fingers to form ears.

 3. Draw features with a toothpick.

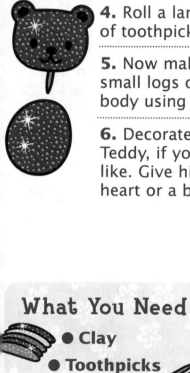 **4.** Roll a larger brown ball for the body. Use a piece of toothpick to stick the head onto the body.

5. Now make the arms and legs. Roll four small logs of brown clay. Stick each onto the body using a piece of toothpick.

6. Decorate Teddy, if you like. Give him a heart or a bow!

What You Need

- **Clay**
- **Toothpicks**

Hello Kitty Goes to School

Help Hello Kitty get ready for school.

What You Do:

 To make **Hello Kitty's backpack**, mold a piece of clay into a shape like this.

 Add a square piece of clay for a flap.

 Press on little strings of clay for buckles.

 Add straps to the backpack, using two twist ties on the back.

What else does Hello Kitty need for school? How about her **lunch box**?

What will Hello Kitty take for a snack? Make her an **apple** to take to school.

Hello Kitty loves to read. To make a **book**, flatten some clay. Use a plastic knife to cut a rectangle.

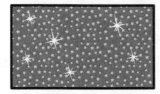

 For the spine, make two lines in the middle with the knife. Then gently fold the book in half. Put a clay picture on the front cover, if you like.

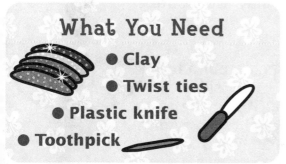

Now make some itty bitty **pencils**. Roll a thin string of clay. Add a pink eraser. Then break off the pointy end of a toothpick. Stick it in the clay for the point on your pencil.

What else? Hello Kitty might need a **ruler** for math. Cut a long, thin rectangle of clay. Use a toothpick to make lines on her ruler.

Make a box of colorful, glittery **crayons** so that Hello Kitty can draw pictures in school.

What You Need

- Clay
- Twist ties
- Plastic knife
- Toothpick

Here's More! Make a desk for Hello Kitty.

Cut two sides of a large, empty matchbox as you see here. Turn the box upside down.

Where are Hello Kitty and her friends going after school?

Turn the page to find out!

Hello Kitty Goes to the Ice Cream Parlor

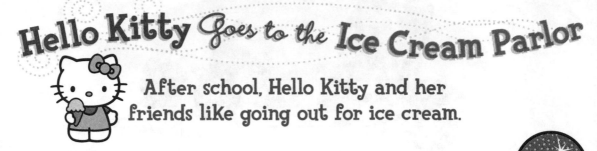

After school, Hello Kitty and her friends like going out for ice cream.

What You Do:

Make **ice cream cones** for Hello Kitty and her friends. Mold a cone using brown

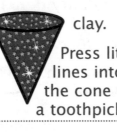

clay. Press little lines into the cone with a toothpick.

What flavor ice cream would Hello Kitty like? Roll some clay into a ball and press it on top of the cone.

To make **swirly-colored ice cream**, partly knead together two different colors of clay.

Add itty-bitty chocolate chips using tiny pieces of brown clay. How about some sprinkles?

Today, Kathy would like an **ice cream sundae**. Roll some clay into a ball. Use your thumb to press a hole in the middle.

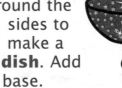

Pinch around the sides to make a **dish**. Add a base.

Add **two scoops of ice cream** to the bowl. What flavors do you think Kathy might like?

Use brown clay to make long drips of **hot fudge**. Spread them over the ice cream.

Would you like to add some **whipped cream**? If so, press some white clay over the hot fudge. Then add a cherry on top!

What You Need

- Clay
- Toothpicks (for pops)

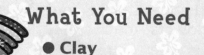

What other kinds of ice cream treats can you make from clay?

Can you guess where Hello Kitty is going next?

Hello Kitty Goes Shopping

Hello Kitty loves to shop!
Help her pick out some outfits.

Hats

1. Trace and cut out one of the hat patterns above. (Or design your own hat for Hello Kitty.)

 **2.** Flatten some clay. Place the pattern on top of the clay and use a plastic knife to cut around it.

3. Now decorate the hat! Make a colored band with a long string of clay. Use the flower cutter to cut out a pretty flower. Press it on the brim. Make your own flowers, too.

4. Let Hello Kitty try on the hat you made for her!

Bows and More

1. Trace and cut out the bow pattern on page 7.

2. Use the pattern to cut out clay bows in lots of different colors!

3. Now to make a sparkly tiara for Hello Kitty, roll a string of clay to fit between Hello Kitty's ears. Decorate it with bows, itty-bitty glittery jewels, or anything else you like!

Purses

1. Mold small pieces of clay into different kinds of purse shapes.

2. Roll a thin string of clay for a handle. For a shoulder strap, try pressing the ends of a twist tie into the top of the purse.

3. Decorate the purses with clay flowers, buttons, or bows. Use a toothpick to draw details.

What You Need

- Hello Kitty full-body clay cutout
- Lightweight paper
- Pencil
- Scissors
- Clay
- Plastic knife
- Flower clay cutter

- Twist ties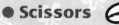
- Toothpick

Hello Kitty Travels

**Whether she sails or flies,
Hello Kitty loves to be on the go!**

What fun on a summer day—Hello Kitty on a sailboat!

What You Do:

1. Roll a thick log of clay. Then press your fingers into the middle of the clay to flatten it.

Pinch around the clay sides to make a boat shape.

2. Cut a triangle from a scrap of paper. Tape or glue it to one end of a twist tie.

3. Press the bottom of the twist tie into the boat. Decorate the sides of the boat, if you like. Then let the clay harden.

What You Need

- **Clay**
- **Scrap of paper**
- **Scissors**
- **Tape or glue**
- **Twist tie**

Blue skies overhead—it's a perfect day for Hello Kitty to take a plane ride!

What You Do:

1. Flatten a piece of clay. Then mold it into a thick heart shape.

2. Press a ball of clay onto the heart, as shown.

3. Fold up each side of the heart. Also fold up the pointy end.

4. Make wings and press them onto each side of the plane.

5. Make the nose of the plane. Press a little ball of clay onto the front of the plane. Then decorate the plane however you like.

6. Use a tooth-pick to poke a hole in the tail of the plane. Then let the clay dry. (If any parts come loose, glue them to the plane.)

7. Cut a banner shape from a scrap of paper. Write a greeting on it. Use a toothpick to poke a hole in one end.

Thread one end of a piece of string through the hole in the banner.

What You Need

- Clay
- Toothpick
- Glue
- Scrap of paper
- Scissors
- Marker
- Piece of thin string, about four inches long

Hello Kitty

Make a knot.
Thread the other end through the hole in the plane's tail. Make another knot.

Hello Kitty Celebrates New Year's Eve

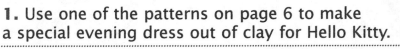

It's New Year's Eve and Hello Kitty gets to stay up until midnight!

1. Use one of the patterns on page 6 to make a special evening dress out of clay for Hello Kitty.

2. Then make Hello Kitty a glittery tiara and evening purse. (See page 25 for ideas.)

3. Make a sparkly wand for Hello Kitty to wave at midnight. Shape a clay star. Stick it on the end of a toothpick. If you like, add streamers by pressing little pieces of ribbon into the back of the star.

What You Need

- **Hello Kitty full-body clay cutout**
- **Lightweight paper**
- **Pencil**
- **Scissors**
- **Clay**
- **Toothpick**
- **Ribbon (optional)**

28

Here's More!
Make a party blower to celebrate New Year's Eve with Hello Kitty!

1. Cut a shape like this from a piece of paper. It should be about two inches wide at the top.

2. Bend a flexible straw like this.

3. Wrap the paper around the bent end of the straw like a funnel. Then tape it in place.

4. Tear itty-bitty pieces of brightly colored paper. Fill the funnel about halfway with the bits of paper.

5. Put the other end of the straw to your lips and blow.

Happy New Year!

(Make sure to clean up afterward!)

What You Need
- **Brightly colored paper**
  - **Scissors**
  - **Flexible straw**
  - **Tape**

Let It Snow!

It's wintertime and Hello Kitty can't wait to ride her sled!

What You Do:

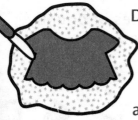

Dress Hello Kitty for a cold, snowy day. Trace and cut out the **coat** pattern shown here. Flatten some clay. Place the pattern on top of the clay and use a plastic knife to cut around it.

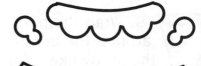

Trace and cut out the **hat** pattern at right.

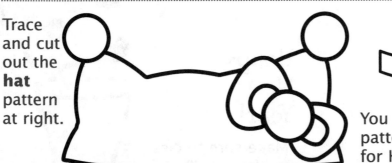

You can trace and cut out the pattern here to make a **scarf** for Hello Kitty.

1. For a **sled,** flatten some clay. Use a plastic knife to cut out a rectangle. Round one end with your fingers.

2. Put two small lumps of clay on the sled, as shown. Stick a large paper clip into each lump of clay.

3. Use a toothpick to poke two holes in the rounded end of the sled. Let the clay dry.

Tip: If the paper clips come loose, attach them to the sled with a bit of glue.

4. Turn the sled over. Glue a toothpick to the sled as shown. Let the glue dry.

5. Thread a piece of yarn or string through the holes. Knot the ends.

What You Need

- **Hello Kitty full-body clay cutout**
- **Lightweight paper**
- **Pencil**
- **Scissors**
- **Clay**
- **Plastic knife**
- **Two large paper clips**
- **Colored toothpicks**
- **Glue**
- **Thin yarn or string**

Now Hello Kitty can go sledding!

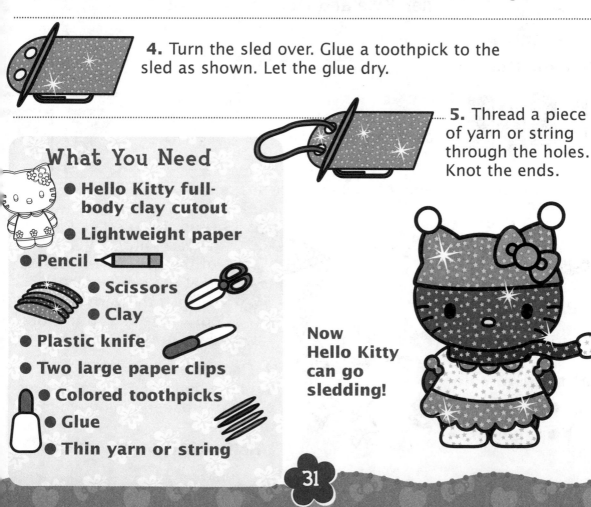

Hello Kitty's Springtime Fun

In the Spring, Hello Kitty likes to fly her kite and ride her scooter.

Making a Kite

What You Do:

1. Flatten four pieces of different-colored clay.

Use a plastic knife to cut out four shapes that look like this.

2. Press the pieces together to make a kite shape.

What You Need

- Clay
- Plastic knife
- Piece of yarn, about six inches long
- Scraps of colored paper
- Scissors
- Glue

3. Add the kite tail. Press the yarn into one end of the kite, on the back. Let the clay harden.
Tip: If the yarn comes loose, attach it to the kite with a bit of glue.

4. Decorate the kite's tail. Cut out little bow shapes from scraps of colored paper. Glue them to the tail.

Hello Kitty, go fly a kite!

Making a Scooter

What You Do:

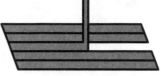

1. Tear off five twist ties but leave them together. Bend up about half of the middle twist tie, as shown.

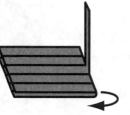

2. Bend the remaining four twist ties underneath, as shown.

3. Wrap another twist tie around the middle twist tie to make a T-shape.

4. Wrap clay all over the twist-tie shape. Add a flower to decorate the handle bars, if you like.

5. Make two round balls for wheels.

6. Let the scooter parts dry. Then glue the wheels to the underside of the scooter.

What You Need

- **Twist ties**
  - **Clay**
  - **Glue**

Now, hop on for a ride, Hello Kitty!

Hello Kitty *Goes to the* Beach

It's a hot summer day and Hello Kitty is off to the beach!

A bathing suit

To make a bathing suit for Hello Kitty to wear, trace and cut out the pattern below.

Flatten a piece of clay. Place the pattern on top of the clay. Then use a plastic knife to cut out the shape. Decorate Hello Kitty's bathing suit with bows, flowers, whatever you like!

A beach towel

Hello Kitty needs a beach towel, too. Make long strings of different-colored clay. Then press them together. Shape the clay into a long rectangle.

A surfboard

Surf's up! Shape a surfboard from a long piece of flattened clay.

A pail

Make a pail. Roll a ball of clay. Use your finger to make a hole in the middle of the ball. Then pinch around the sides to make a pail shape.

Press down gently on the pail so that it can stand. Add a thin string of clay for a handle.

A shovel

For a shovel, break off the end of a toothpick. Press a piece of clay around the end.

A beach ball

Make a colorful beach ball by kneading together different colors of clay. Stop mixing them when you have a pretty pattern. Then roll the clay into a ball.

Don't forget your sunscreen, Hello Kitty!

Here's More!
Make a sandy beach for Hello Kitty.

1. Cut a wavy shape from a piece of sandpaper. Fold back one edge, as shown.

2. Tape or glue the flat edge to another piece of sandpaper. Now you have sand dunes!

3. Arrange the things you made for Hello Kitty on the beach.

What You Need

- **Hello Kitty full-body clay cutout**
- **Lightweight paper**
- **Pencil**
- **Scissors**
- **Clay**
- **Plastic knife**
- **Toothpicks**

Happy Birthday, Hello Kitty!

 November 1st is Hello Kitty's birthday. Her family is planning her party. *Shhh!* It's a surprise!

A crown

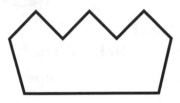

Make a birthday crown for Hello Kitty to wear. Trace and cut out the pattern here. Flatten a piece of clay. Put the pattern on the clay and use a plastic knife to cut out the shape.

 Decorate the crown with polka dots, flowers, bows, or other designs. Let it dry.

A birthday cake

Now make Hello Kitty's birthday cake. Roll a ball of clay.

 Press down on it gently to flatten the top and bottom.

Decorate the cake! Use a toothpick to make designs in the clay. Add clay flowers and other decorations.

 Don't forget the candles! Break toothpicks in half and stick them around the cake.

A pretty plate

Make a pretty plate to put the cake on. Take a ball of clay and flatten it.

Flatten a second ball of clay and press your flower cutter into it.

Gently press the flower-shaped clay on top of the round clay like this.

The birthday surprise cake is ready for Hello Kitty!

What else? Try making balloons, party blowers, and presents like the ones below.

What You Need

- **Hello Kitty full-body clay cutout**
- **Lightweight paper**
- **Pencil**
  - **Scissors**
  - **Clay**
  - **Plastic knife**
  - **Colored toothpicks**
  - **Flower cutter**
- **Thin string (optional)**

Design a special party dress for Hello Kitty to wear using one of the patterns on page 6.

Home Sweet Home

Hello Kitty loves her home.

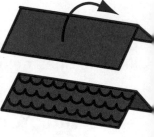

A house

What You Do:

1. To make a house, tape together two shoe boxes, as shown.

2. Fold a sheet of construction paper into a roof shape. Then draw tiles on the roof with a marker or crayon.

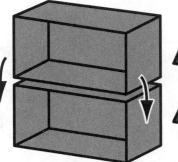

3. Attach a red paper chimney to the roof with tape.

4. Then attach the roof to the house.

5. Use glue to cover the rest of the outside of the house with red construction paper.

6. Now it's time to decorate! Cover the floors with scraps of gift wrap that have a pretty pattern.

7. Add the furniture you made throughout this book.

Here's More! Hello Kitty would love to curl up and read a book in this cozy chair!

A cozy chair

1. Fold some news-paper into a small, thick rectangle.

2. Cover the newspaper with clay. Then fold it like this.

3. For the arms of the chair, break off two pieces from a log of clay. Use a piece of toothpick to stick each arm onto the chair.

What You Need

- **Two shoe boxes**
- **Red construction paper**
- **Markers or crayons**
  - **Tape**
  - **Glue**
  - **Scissors**
  - **Scraps of gift wrap**
- **Newspaper**
- **Toothpicks**
- **Paper doily**

4. Flatten little balls of lay to make plump pillows. Use a toothpick to draw designs on them.

5. Cut a lacy piece from a paper doily. Glue it to the back of the chair when the clay is dry.

You have made such wonderful stuff for Hello Kitty.
Now you can make great Hello Kitty things for yourself!

Hello Kitty *and* Kathy Pencil Toppers

Make these handy pencil toppers
and Hello Kitty and Kathy can help you with homework!

What You Do:

1. Use one of your cutters to make two of the same clay shapes.

2. Press the eraser end of a pencil into one of the shapes, about halfway.

3. Press the second cutout on top of the first one. Line up the shapes. Then press the edges together. Let the clay dry.

What You Need

- **Hello Kitty head cutter or Kathy head cutter**
- **Clay**
- **Pencil**

Neat Hello Kitty Necklaces

Hello Kitty and Kathy can hang around with you anytime when you wear these necklaces!

What You Do:

1. Use one of your cutters to make a shape.

2. Use a toothpick to poke a hole in the shape.

3. Let the clay dry. Then thread a piece of yarn or ribbon through the hole and knot the ends.

Make more necklaces using your other cutters!

What You Need

- **Hello Kitty head cutter or Kathy head cutter**
- **Toothpick**
- **Two-foot length of yarn or ribbon**

Hello Kitty Message Magnets

Make a Hello Kitty magnet to hold important messages on your family's fridge!

What You Do:

Use one of your cutters to press out a shape from clay. Let it dry completely.

Glue the magnet to the back of the cutout shape. Let the glue dry completely.

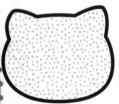

What You Need

- **Assorted Hello Kitty cutters**
- **Clay**
- **Small round magnet or a small piece of flexible magnet strip**
- **Glue**

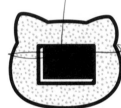

NOTE to ME:

Make Hello Kitty gift for Mom tonight!!

Hello Kitty Clay Recipe

When you need more clay, mix up a batch
of this easy homemade recipe.

What You Do:

1. Mix together the flour and salt in a bowl.

2. Add the oil and water. Mix well with a large spoon.
Add a pinch of glitter, if you like.

3. Knead the clay until it holds together. Add a little
more flour if the clay is sticky. Add a few drops of
water if it is too dry.

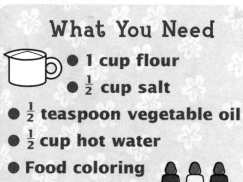

What You Need

- **1 cup flour**
- **$\frac{1}{2}$ cup salt**
- **$\frac{1}{2}$ teaspoon vegetable oil**
- **$\frac{1}{2}$ cup hot water**
- **Food coloring**
- **Bowl**
- **Large spoon**
- **Glitter (optional)**

4. To color the clay, divide it into
sections. Add a few drops of food
coloring to each piece. Knead the
clay until the color is well blended.
(Instead of coloring the clay, you
can paint it with poster paints
after the clay has dried.)

5. Store in a self-closing
plastic bag.

Conclusion

As you have seen from the projects in this book, you can make so many cute things for Hello Kitty out of clay and simple stuff you have around your house. But don't stop here. There are lots more fun-filled adventures awaiting Hello Kitty! How about sending Hello Kitty and her pals to summer camp, or on a trip around the world, or into outer space? Using your imagination, the possibilities are endless!